CONTENTS

CAST OF CHARACTERS: .... PAGE 08

ACT 1: .... PAGE 10

ACT 2: .... PAGE 32

ACT 3: .... PAGE 50

ACT 4: .... PAGE 64

ACT 5: .... PAGE 70

ABOUT THE RETELLING
AUTHOR AND ILLUSTRATORS: .... PAGE 78

ABOUT WILLIAM SHAKESPEARE: .... PAGE 80

THE HISTORY BEHIND THE PLAY: .... PAGE 81

SHAKESPEAREAN LANGUAGE: .... PAGE 82

DISCUSSION QUESTIONS: .... PAGE 84

WRITING PROMPTS: .... PAGE 85

SHAKESPEARE'S

ROMEO

&

JULIET

RETOLD BY
MARTIN POWELL

ILLUSTRATED BY
EVA CABRERA

COLOURED BY
JORGE GONZALEZ

Raintree

www.raintreepublishers.co.uk
Visit our website to find out
more information about
Raintree books.

To order:
☎ Phone 0845 6044371
🖥 Fax +44 (0) 1865 312263
✉ Email myorders@raintreepublishers.co.uk

Customers from outside the UK please telephone +44 1865 312262

Raintree is an imprint of Capstone Global Library Limited, a company incorporated in
England and Wales having its registered office at 7 Pilgrim Street, London, EC4V 6LB –
Registered company number: 6695582

Text © Stone Arch Books 2012
First published in the United Kingdom by
Capstone Global Library Ltd in 2012
The moral rights of the proprietor have been asserted.

Art Director: Kay Fraser
Graphic Designer: Hilary Wacholz
Editor: Diyan Leake
Production Specialist: Victoria Fitzgerald
Originated by Capstone Global Library Ltd
Printed in and bound by Grafos, Barcelona in Spain

ISBN 978 1 406 24329 1
16 15
10 9 8 7 6 5 4 3

British Library Cataloguing in Publication Data
A full catalogue record for this book is available from the British Library.

SHAKESPEARE

WILLIAM SHAKESPEARE WAS ONE OF
THE GREATEST WRITERS THE WORLD
HAS EVER KNOWN.

HE WROTE COMEDIES, TRAGEDIES,
HISTORIES, AND ROMANCES ABOUT
ANCIENT HEROES, BRUTAL WARS,
AND MAGICAL CREATURES.

THIS IS ONE OF THOSE STORIES.

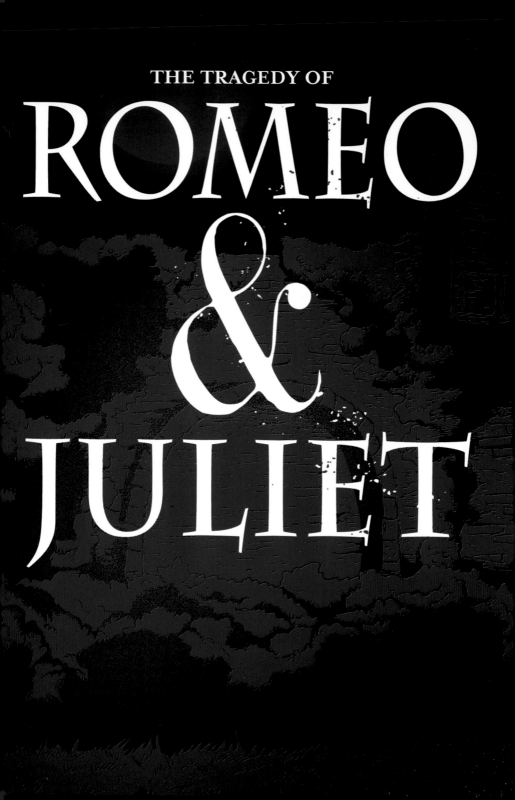

THE TRAGEDY OF
ROMEO
&
JULIET

THE CAST

TYBALT

NURSE

JULIET

MERCUTIO   BENVOLIO

FRIAR
LAURENCE

ROMEO

"A pair of star-cross'd lovers . . ."

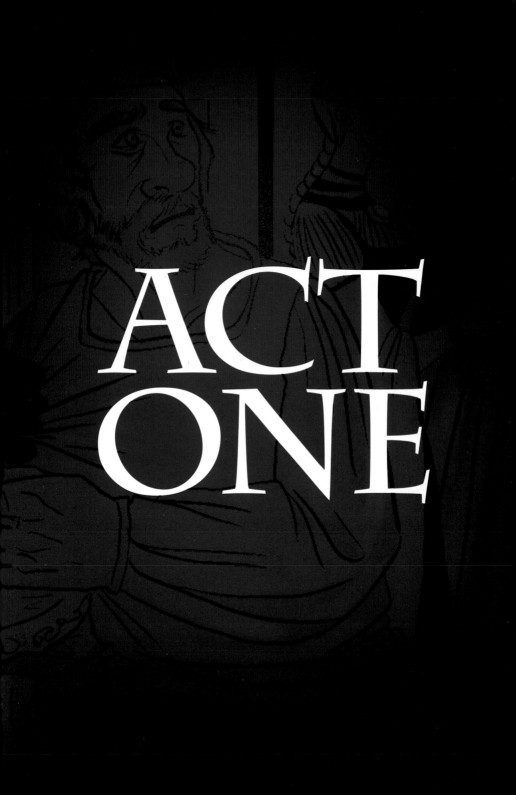

The city of Verona, Italy, in the early 14th century.

The Montagues and the Capulets, two rich and powerful families, were in a bitter and bloody feud.

This feud set in motion the tragic tale of Romeo and Juliet, *a pair of star cross'd lovers . . .*

We serve as good a man as you do!

Ah! Two men from the House of Montague are here! Do you wish to fight, you dogs?

Ha! Fight then, if you be men!

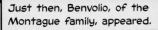
Just then, Benvolio, of the Montague family, appeared.

Stop, you fools! Put away your swords!

WOOOoosh!!

Tybalt Capulet then challenged Benvolio.

Face me, Benvolio, and prepare to die!

I only want to keep the peace, Tybalt. Put away your sword.

Peace?! I hate that word as I hate all Montagues!

Fight me, coward!

13

Because of the prince's actions, peace was kept. But hatred still burned in the hearts of the Capulets and Montagues.

Where is our son, Romeo, my lord? I am glad he was not at this fight.

Romeo is so sad these days. If we could only learn why his sorrows grow, we could help give him a cure.

Romeo's sad wanderings brought him to the very spot where his parents had just been . . .

Good day, Romeo!

Dear cousin, was that my father and mother that just left?

Later, Capulet spoke with Paris, a young man from a wealthy family.

Lord Capulet, do you give me permission to marry your daughter, Juliet?

If you win her heart, you shall have my consent.

Tonight we hold a feast with many guests. You, too, are most welcome, Paris.

Servant! Find those persons whose names are on this list and tell them the House of Capulet requests their presence.

But Lord Capulet did not know that his servant could not read.

A single glance at Juliet,
and Romeo fell in love . . .

I never saw true beauty 'til this night.

This, by his voice, be a Montague!

Give me my sword, boy.

SshING!

Now, by the honour of my kin, to strike him dead, I hold it not a sin!

My cousin Tybalt, what is the matter?!

"O Romeo, Romeo!
Wherefore art thou
Romeo?"

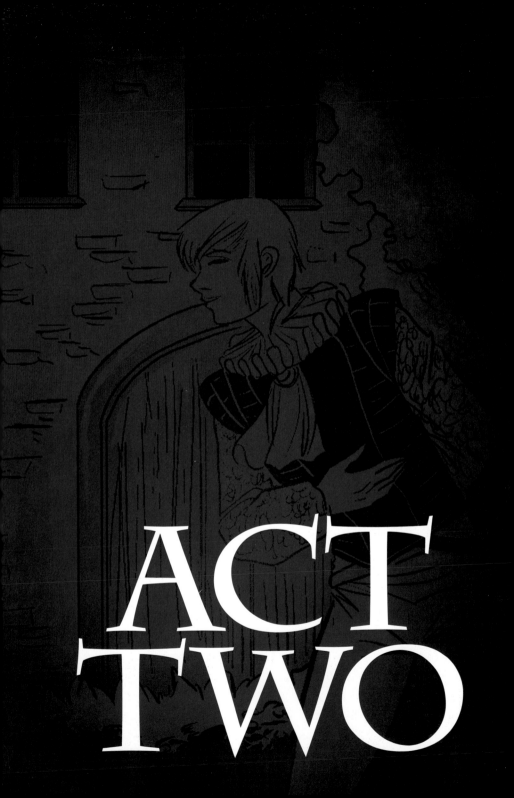

What light through yonder window breaks?

It is the east, and Juliet is the sun!

See, how she leans her cheek upon her hand! Oh, that I were a glove upon that hand, that I might touch that cheek!

I take you at your word. Call me your love; from then onward, I will never be Romeo.

My ears have not yet heard a hundred words from you, yet I know your voice.

Are you not Romeo and a Montague?

Neither, fair saint, if either you dislike.

The next day, Romeo visited Friar Laurence for advice . . .
Good morning, Friar Laurence.
Young Romeo, you must be ill to rise from bed so early.
Or if not, then Romeo has not been in bed tonight.
I have not rested yet. I was feasting with my enemy.
What do you mean, my boy?
My heart's love is set on the fair daughter of rich Capulet.
I hope that you will agree to marry us today.

Nurse, help me see my lady. Tell her to find a way to come to St. Pietro's church this afternoon . . .

. . . and there, with Friar Laurence's blessing, we shall be married.

I will tell her. She will be a joyful woman!

The nurse hurried back to Juliet.

HUFF HUFF

Your Romeo asks, like an honest gentleman, and a kind and handsome one . . .

. . . that you meet him at Friar Laurence's cell. There, Romeo waits to make you his wife!

Oh, good news!

URK!

That evening, in Friar Laurence's cell . . .

ACT THREE

"A plague o' both
the houses!"

So, in secret, Romeo and Juliet were married.

Early the next morning, the young married couple prepared for Romeo's tragic exile . . .

Night's candles have burnt out, and day rises over the mountain tops. I must be gone and live, or stay and die.

Let me be caught, let me be put to death, I love you so.

Oh, now be gone; the daylight grows.

Oh, Romeo, will we ever meet again?

I do not doubt it.

"Hold, daughter. I do spy a kind of hope . . ."

ACT FOUR

The next morning . . .

Help, oh please someone help!

What is the matter, nurse?

Oh, sad day! Juliet is dead!

Oh, my child, my only life!

The friar's plan had worked. All of Juliet's family thought she was dead.

ACT FIVE

"For never was a story of
more woe than this of Juliet
and her Romeo."

Then, in the depths of Juliet's tomb . . .

Oh, my love! My wife! I will stay with you now, and never leave again!

Eyes, take your last look! Arms, take your last embrace!

Here's to my love!

And with a kiss, I die.

ABOUT THE RETELLING AUTHOR

Since 1986, **Martin Powell** has been a freelance writer. He has written hundreds of stories, many of which have been published by Disney, Marvel, Tekno Comix, Moonstone Books, and others. In 1989, Powell received an Eisner Award nomination for his graphic novel *Scarlet in Gaslight*. This award is one of the highest comic book honours.

ABOUT THE ILLUSTRATORS

Eva Cabrera is a sequential artist born in Jalapa, Veracruz, Mexico. She is currently the Art Director of Neggi Studio (video games) and an illustrator at Zombie Studio. She also illustrates comic books and is the main artist for *El Arsenal: Been Caught Stealing*. She has won several comic-related competitions and has participated in various art expos. In her spare time, Eva feeds her addiction to coffee and the internet.

Jorge Gonzalez was born in Monterrey, Mexico, in 1982. Since then, he has dedicated several years of his life to the comic book industry. Jorge began his career as a colourist for the graphic novel retellings of *The Time Machine* and *Journey to the Centre of the Earth*.

ABOUT WILLIAM SHAKESPEARE

William Shakespeare's true date of birth is unknown, but it is celebrated on 23 April 1564. He was born in Stratford-upon-Avon in Warwickshire and was the third of eight children to his parents, John and Mary.

At the age of 18, William married a woman named Anne Hathaway on 27 November 1582. He and Anne had three children together, including twins. After that point, Shakespeare's history is somewhat of a mystery. Not much is known about this period of his life, until 1592 when his plays first graced theatre stages in London.

From 1594 onwards, Shakespeare performed his plays with a stage company called the Lord Chamberlain's Men (later known as the King's Men). They soon became the top playing company in all of London, earning the favour of Queen Elizabeth I and King James I along the way.

Shakespeare retired in 1613, and died at the age of 52 on 23 April 1616. He was buried at Holy Trinity Church in Stratford. The epitaph on his grave curses any person who disturbs it. Translated to modern English, part of it reads:

> Blessed be the man that spares these stones,
> And cursed be he who moves my bones.

Over a period of 25 years, Shakespeare wrote more than 40 works, including poems, plays, and prose. His plays have been performed all over the world and translated to every major language.

THE HISTORY BEHIND THE PLAY

Romeo and Juliet is one of Shakespeare's most popular plays. It was written sometime between the years 1591 and 1595.

Shakespeare's *Romeo and Juliet* was inspired by several old, tragic love stories. One of these is an Italian tale written in 1562, called *The Tragical History of Romeus and Juliet*. Another is called "Pyramus and Thisbe", from Ovid's *Metamorphoses*, which is also performed as a play-within-a-play in Shakespeare's *A Midsummer Night's Dream*.

This play contains several soliloquies (speeches where a character speaks out loud to himself or herself). When Juliet starts to speak her soliloquy on page 36, she does not know Romeo is listening. He, too, gives a soliloquy, starting on page 34, before talking to Juliet.

Most of the early performances of Shakespeare's plays featured only male actors. The roles of female characters such as Juliet were played by men who wore wigs and dresses.

Romeo and Juliet is one of the most popular plays of all time. Even today, it is performed in theatres all over the world. *Romeo and Juliet* has also been made into several films, musicals, ballets, operas – and graphic novels like this one.

SHAKESPEAREAN LANGUAGE

Shakespeare's writing is powerful and memorable – and sometimes difficult to understand. Many lines in his plays can be read in different ways or can have multiple meanings. Also, English spelling and pronunciation have changed over time, so the way he spelled words was not always the same as the way we spell them now. However, Shakespeare still influences the way we write and speak today. Below are some of his more famous phrases that have also become part of our language.

FAMOUS LINES FROM ROMEO & JULIET

"A pair of star-cross'd lovers . . ." (Prologue)

SPEAKER: Chorus

MODERN INTERPRETATION: **A pair of young people fall in love and suffer because fate is against them.**

EXPLANATION: Long ago, people believed that our fates were written in the stars. In this line, the chorus (or narrator) explains that the stars have turned against Romeo and Juliet's love, dooming their relationship from the start.

"O Romeo, Romeo! Wherefore art thou Romeo?"
(Act II, Scene II)

SPEAKER: Juliet

MODERN INTERPRETATION: **Oh, Romeo, why do you have to be Romeo Montague?**

EXPLANATION: Juliet, a Capulet, wishes that Romeo was not a Montague. She is unaware that he is nearby, listening to her soliloquy. Also, "wherefore" does not mean "where" as many people mistakenly believe – it actually means "why".

"A plague o' both the houses!" (Act III, Scene I)

SPEAKER: Mercutio

MODERN INTERPRETATION: **May a plague (sickness), curse both of your families.**

EXPLANATION: Mercutio, after being stabbed by Tybalt Capulet because Romeo Montague interfered, blames both their feuding families for his death.

"Hold, daughter. I do spy a kind of hope . . ." (Act IV, Scene I)

SPEAKER: Friar Laurence

MODERN INTERPRETATION: **Wait a second, young lady, I see some hope.**

EXPLANATION: Friar Laurence attempts to calm Juliet by telling her that there is still hope for her and Romeo's love. He then warns her that it will be dangerous, and they must act quickly.

"For never was a story of more woe than this of Juliet and her Romeo." (Act V, Scene III)

SPEAKER: The prince

MODERN INTERPRETATION: **There was never a story with more pain and suffering than the story of Romeo and Juliet's relationship.**

EXPLANATION: The prince explains that the tragic tale of Romeo and Juliet's love, and their sad deaths, is made even more tragic by the unlucky circumstances surrounding them.

DISCUSSION QUESTIONS

1. Romeo and Juliet fall in love at first sight. Do you believe in love at first sight? Why or why not?

2. This graphic novel has many illustrations. Which page is your favourite? Why?

3. Juliet's parents don't approve of her love of Romeo. Does your family disapprove of anything you do?

WRITING PROMPTS

1. The Capulets and the Montagues hate each other. Can you think of some ways for the two families to learn to get along? What would you do if you were Romeo or Juliet? Write about how you'd put an end to the family feud.

2. Romeo and Juliet meet at a costume ball, or party. Imagine that you're going to attend a costume party. What kind of outfit would you wear? Write about it, then draw a picture of yourself in your outfit.

3. Which character is most to blame for the deaths of Romeo and Juliet? Was it Friar Laurence? Tybalt? Romeo? Juliet? Someone else? Explain your answer.